This book belongs to

....

This edition published by Parragon Books Ltd in 2017

Parragon Books Ltd
Chartist House
15–17 Trim Street
Bath BA1 1HA, UK
www.parragon.com

ISBN 978-1-4748-7685-8

Printed in Italy

ANNUAL 2018

PaRragon

Bath • New York • Cologne • Melbourne • Delhi
Hong Kong • Shenzhen • Singapore

Contents

Meet the PAW Patrol team

Whenever there is trouble, PAW Patrol rush to the rescue. The pups are raring to go, go, go!

Skye

Ryder

Rocky

Tracker

Chase

Marshall

Zuma

Rubble

Everest

To the skies!

It's time to take off – one of the pups needs back-up! Before Chase can soar to the rescue, he needs to work out who has made a yelp for help.

Follow the cloud trails with your finger, then colour in the right pup picture at the end.

① ② ③

Pup, pup and away!

a

b

c

9

Answers on page 68.

Puppy power!

The PAW Patrol are always ready for some super sports action! Get out your brightest pencils or crayons, then colour the champs in.

Game on!

Fun at the farm

Skye is lending a paw to Farmer Yumi! Draw lines to match up the missing pieces to the correct places in the picture.

1
2
3
4
5

Answers on page 68.

Chase
in the race!

Chase is a top police dog. Whether it's directing the traffic, tracking down trouble or sniffing out clues, he's the pup to call!

Ready for action!

Did you know?

Chase is a German shepherd pup.

Chase is ... smart and organized.

Chase has ... a super sense of smell.

Chase can ... save the day!

02

PUPPY POWER!

Net shoots out to catch falling objects.

Searchlight is used for rescues after dark.

Megaphone helps with directing traffic.

Tricky tick test

How well do you know Chase? Use this quiz to find out!

1 **What does Chase's Pup House change into?**

a A speed boat ◯
b A police car ◯
c A parachute ◯

2 **What is the shape on Chase's pup badge?**

a A square ◯
b A heart ◯
c A star ◯

3 **What colour flashes are on Chase's Pup Pack?**

a Blue and red ◯
b Blue and green ◯
c Blue and pink ◯

13

Answers on page 68.

Save the day!

Ryder has fallen down a hole. He needs a super pup to lend a paw! Can you help Rubble dig a path to find him?

You can move through the maze, but you must only step on the yellow squares.

Start digging

Finish

Answers on page 68.

Seaside spotting

The Cap'n is practising his memory skills. Would you like to try, too? Ask a grown-up to set a timer to one minute.

Now look at the picture closely, taking in every detail.

When your time is up, turn over!

The quiz is on the next page.

Seaside spotting

Are you ready to put your memory skills to the test? Find a pen or pencil, then take the quiz.

The seaside scene is on page 15.

1 How many seagulls are there?

a One ○
b Four ○
c Five ○

4 What object is lying on the sand?

a A rubber ring ○
b A telescope ○
c A picnic hamper ○

2 Which pup is travelling over the water?

a Tracker ○
b Everest ○
c Zuma ○

5 What colour is the dinghy?

a Red and white ○
b Yellow and blue ○
c Yellow and red ○

3 What is the weather like?

a Sunny ○
b Snowy ○
c Rainy ○

6 Which pup is playing with the rope?

a Skye ○
b Rocky ○
c Chase ○

No peeping at the picture ... Marshall *is* watching!

Answers on page 68.

Doggy day off

The PAW Patrol work hard and play hard, too. Can you finish off this picture of Marshall and Rubble playing in the Lookout?

Use the number key to help you choose the right colours.

1	brown	4	red
2	dark red	5	pink
3	yellow	6	grey

One of the PAW Patrol pups is feeling hungry. Look at the bowl and then decide who has got a rumbly tummy.

Answers on page 68.

Pups save a monkeynaut

Ryder, Zuma and Rocky were fishing on the jetty. Suddenly a strange capsule tumbled out of the sky, landing in the ocean with a splash!

"I dreamed that I just saw a UFO," yawned Zuma.

"That wasn't a dream," replied Ryder. "Let's check it out!"

The pups raced across the water.

"It's a real-deal spaceship," said Zuma.

Bang! Bang! Bang!

"Listen," whispered Ryder. "Someone is trapped inside!"

Rocky opened the hatch on the side of the craft. A tiny space traveller appeared.

"Welcome!" said Ryder. "We are your friends."

The pups towed the capsule back to the dock. Cap'n Turbot was on his boat, eating a banana. The space traveller grabbed the snack and started munching.

"It's a monkey-astronaut?" gasped the Cap'n.

Rocky nodded.

"It's a monkeynaut!"

The mission controller's face flashed up on a screen inside the capsule. Ryder explained what had happened.

"That monkey is Captain Gordie," replied the mission controller, "and now he can't get up into orbit in time to meet the space station. With no monkey, there's no mission."

Ryder jumped up. This was a job for PAW Patrol!

"We'll launch the space capsule from the Air Patroller," announced Ryder. "But first we need a rocket to power the capsule into space."

There was an abandoned cabin in the woods. Rocky could reuse the cabin's tin roof to make a rocket. Rubble's crane would be able to lift it off.

The pups got to work. PAW Patrol was on a roll!

Ryder, Rocky and Rubble zoomed to the abandoned cabin.

"Rubble," ordered Ryder. "Load the tin from this roof into Rocky's truck."

"Will do!" barked Rubble.

Ryder took Rocky over to a rusty pick-up van. It was full of old parts that could be reused for the rocket.

"Lots of good stuff here!" grinned Rocky.

As soon as they were ready, Rubble carried the tin and truck parts to the beach. Rocky started building an awesome new rocket! Ryder and the pups fixed the rocket to the back of the space capsule.

"It looks terrific," decided Ryder. "Now we just need the monkeynaut!"

Ryder called the PAW Patrol.
    "We're on our way," nodded Chase.
    Next, Ryder made contact with Robo-dog in the Air Patroller.
    "Meet us at the beach," he said.

Ryder and the pups helped the monkeynaut back into his capsule, then climbed aboard the Air Patroller.

"Oh no!"

The monkeynaut had spotted Cap'n Turbot's banana! Gordie reached out to grab it, knocking a screw out of the space capsule's hatch.

The Air Patroller started to pull the capsule into the air.

"Wait!" shouted Cap'n Turbot. "Stop!"

Ryder sent Rocky out to fix the broken hatch. "Green means go!"

Rocky was just getting to work, when the monkeynaut pulled him inside.

"Adventure Bay, we have a problem," he barked. "I'm trapped!"

Ryder frowned. Only one pup could reach the capsule now.

"Got to fly!" cried Skye.

Skye used her wing tip like a tool to unjam the hatch and free Rocky. Captain Gordie was off!

"If ever you're in a space jam," grinned Ryder, "just yelp for help!"

THE END

Kitty-tastrophe

Look who's been getting up to mischief on these pages! Can you race to the rescue?

1

Ryder's pup treats have gone missing. Draw a biscuit for each pup.

Grab a pencil and use your sketching skills to put things right.

2 The colours have disappeared from Skye's Pup Pup Boogie game! Can you put them back in again?

3

Rubble's rubber ring has got a puncture! Use your brightest crayons or pencils to add colour and make the ring safe again.

4

Brrr! Jake has lost a woolly sock. Sketch a new one to make a matching pair.

5

Where has Chase's toy gone? Draw in a Frisbee for the pup to catch.

Marshall
on a mission!

Marshall is the PAW Patrol team's brave firedog. This pup is raring, daring and always ready to roll!

Ruff-ruff rescue!

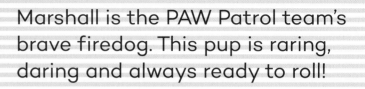

Did you know?

Marshall can't help being a little bit clumsy!

Marshall is ... brave and adventurous.

Marshall has ... a fire station Pup House.

Marshall can ... put out flames, fast!

03

PUPPY POWER!

Double-spray **fire hose** shoots out water.

Super-tough **helmet** is fitted with a torch.

Firedog **collar** and badge.

Animal emergency

Ryder has sent Marshall to rescue an animal in trouble. Which creature needs the pup's help? Read the clues and then put a tick in the right circle.

a○   b○   c○   d○

1 I am only small.

2 I don't have any fur.

3 I walk on four legs.

29

Answers on page 68.

My PAWfect pal

Ever wondered which PAW Patrol pup is most like you? Use this quiz to find out! Work down the list, putting a circle around the letter you like the best each time.

1 **Puppy fun ...**

a A winter walk.
b A tickle fight.
c A treasure hunt.

2 **Puppy food ...**

a Jacket potato.
b Fish fingers.
c Baked beans.

3 **Puppy holidays ...**

a The mountains.
b The beach.
c The city.

4 **Puppy mottos ...**

a Off the trail, I won't fail!
b Let's dive in!
c Don't trash it, stash it!

5 **Puppy hobbies ...**

a Snowboarding.
b Swimming.
c Junk modelling.

6 **Puppy bedtimes ...**

a A snuggly blanket.
b A funny storybook.
c A twinkly night light.

Mostly As

You're a playful pup with a taste for adventure, just like Everest!

Mostly Bs

You and Zuma are the fun-loving jokers in the pack!

Mostly Cs

Rocky is clever and creative – and so are you!

Pup House puzzle

At the end of a busy day, the PAW Patrol pups like to curl up in their Pup Houses.

Draw lines to match each team member to the right Pup House.

1

2

3

4

5

a

b

c

d

e

Answers on page 68.

31

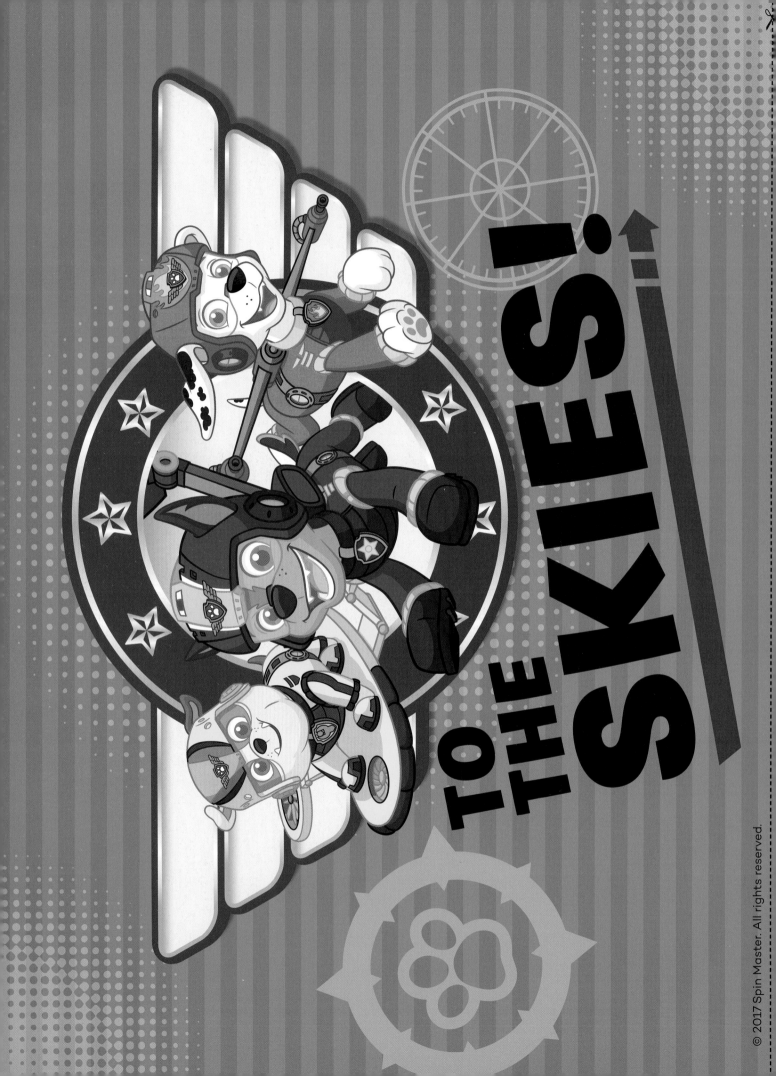

TO THE SKIES!

Cal-amity!

Cali the cat has gone missing in the mountains. Can you spot her hiding in the picture below?

Only one of these badges belongs to Everest. Which one is it?

a

b

c

Answers on page 68.

Rocky
to the rescue!

Rocky isn't just ready to rescue, he wants to reuse and recycle, too. The pup can make brilliant vehicles and gadgets out of the rubbish that he finds.

Green means go!

Did you know?

Rocky doesn't like getting his fur wet!

Rocky is ... clever and creative.

Rocky has ... a toolkit in his Pup Pack.

Rocky can ... turn trash into treasure!

05

PUPPY POWER!

Bright orange **utility arm**.

Mechanical claw can pick up litter.

Special **recycling badge**.

New words for old

Rocky loves making new things. Read the clues and then change one letter each time to make three brand new words.

PET ➡ Someone who helps poorly animals. ➡ _ _ _

DOG ➡ Make a hole in the ground. ➡ _ _ _

CAT ➡ A tin that stores food. ➡ _ _ _

41

Answers on page 69.

Park patrol!

Chase is on patrol at the Pup Park today. Give the police pup some colour.

Copy the colours from the little picture of Chase!

Count the carrots

The pups have a fluffy new friend! Can you count all the carrots, before the bunny munches them?

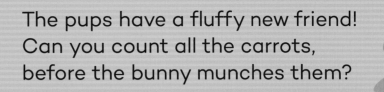

I can count

_____

carrots!

Answers on page 69.

Wags and gags

Marshall's jokes always get the PAW Patrol pups giggling! Here are some of his best howlers. Can you think of any of your own?

What kind of dog loves to take bubble baths?

A shampoodle!

What is a terrier's favourite city?

New Yorkie!

What do you call a doggy magician?

A Labracadabrador!

What do you get if you cross a yellow dog with a telephone?

A golden receiver!

Why can't Dalmatians hide?

Because they're always spotted.

How do you know when it's raining cats and dogs?

When you step in a poodle!

What do you call a dog that's been out in the cold?

A pupsicle!

Jungle explorer

Tracker loves running in the jungle. What will the pup find here today? Draw in some leaves, flowers and amazing jungle animals.

Now colour Tracker in!

Here comes Rubble!

Rubble is a tough, gruff construction bulldog. This pup can build anything! Rubble will dig, lift and roll until the job is done.

Rubble on the double!

Did you know?

Rubble likes going for rides on his skateboard.

Rubble is ... kind and helpful.

Rubble has ... super-strong muscles.

Rubble can ... move mud, bricks and timber.

Bucket shovel for digging holes.

Hard hat protects Rubble's head.

Handy **tools** for making repairs.

Bubbles for Rubble

After a hard day's work, Rubble loves to relax in a warm bath at Katie's Pet Parlour! Can you draw a bubble path for the pampered pup?

Pup puppets

Let's put on a PAW Patrol show! These finger puppets are so easy to make. Pick your favourite pup or cut out and keep the whole team.

You will need:

- A few sheets of paper in assorted colours
- Pencil
- Scissors
- Sticky tape
- Glue

Yelp for help!

Get some grown-up help before you start this craft activity. Scissors can be sharp.

What to do:

1
Pick a pup from the opposite page, then choose a sheet of paper in a shade that roughly matches their fur colour or PAW Patrol uniform.

2
Draw a rectangle onto the paper that is roughly 10 centimetres wide and 8 centimetres tall. Cut the rectangle out.

3
Wrap the rectangle around your finger, then ask a grown-up to sticky tape the long edge so that it becomes a tube.

4
Carefully cut out the front and the back of the pup from the shapes on the opposite page.

5
Glue the front and the back of the pup onto the tube, pop your finger inside and get ready to play!

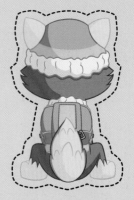

! Make sure that you have finished looking at page 50 before you cut out the shapes on this page.

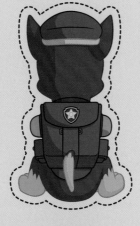

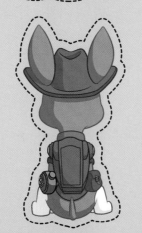

Zuma zooms in!

Zuma is a water-pup, who is calm, loyal and kind. When adventure calls, the PAW Patrol know they can count on Zuma to dive in!

Ready, set, get wet!

Did you know?

Zuma is the youngest pup in the PAW Patrol team.

Zuma is ... playful and fun-loving.

Zuma has ... a smart hovercraft.

Zuma can ... rescue on land or in the water!

PUPPY POWER!

Portable **air tank** for undersea rescues.

Bone-shaped doggy breathing mask.

Water jets to power through water.

Puppy playtime

Zuma is having some time-out with his PAW Patrol buddies. Who can they be? Look at the mixed-up picture, and shout out the names of the pups you can see.

Answers on page 69.

Tracker joins the pups

Carlos was at a jungle temple. A monkey scampered on the sand beside him.

"Hello, Mandy!" said Carlos.

Carlos uncovered a stone lid. When he lifted it, a giant statue appeared.

"Wow!" cried Carlos. "Time to call the PAW Patrol."

Ryder and his friends were out fishing when they got Carlos's call.

"Legend has it that a lost tribe of monkeys has been waiting for their ruler to someday return," explained Cap'n Turbot.

Mandy climbed onto the statue.
She plucked a golden crown
from the top.

"Hey!" shouted Carlos. "That's not
a toy!"

Mandy dropped the crown.
Carlos tried to chase after it, but
he tripped and fell into a deep hole.

"Help!"

On the other side of the jungle, a pup
pricked up his ears.

"That sounds like trouble," he said,
"and it's coming from over there!"

Ryder and the pups scrambled into the PAW Patroller.

"We've got to save Carlos," said Ryder. "Let's go!"

A furry face peered down at Carlos.

"Hello!" said the pup. "My name is Tracker."

"I'm stuck down here!" cried Carlos.

Tracker used his nose to sniff out Carlos's mobile phone. He pressed a button with his paw.

"Drive to the stinky bush and turn right," he told the PAW Patrol. "Hurry!"

A big snake slithered down from a tree ... straight towards Tracker! The plucky pup tried to distract it, but the PAW Patroller arrived just in time to scare the snake away.

"PAW Patrol is on a roll!" shouted Ryder.

The pups sprang into action. Chase lowered his winch into the hole, then lifted Carlos out.

"I am so happy that you are okay!" said Tracker.

"Thanks to you," smiled Carlos.

Tracker
takes the lead!

Tracker is the newest member of the PAW Patrol team. The pup lives in the jungle with Carlos, but when duty calls Tracker always comes running!

I'm all ears!

Did you know?

Tracker's large ears help him to pick up the tiniest sounds.

Tracker is ... thoughtful and quick-witted.

Tracker has ... an off-road jungle jeep.

Tracker can ... swing through the trees!

08

60

PUPPY POWER!

Multi-tool kit for cutting and fixing.

Arm extends to reach tall trees.

Swinging **cables** shoot out from either side.

Furry friends

Tracker is so pleased to be part of the PAW Patrol team! Grab your crayons or pencils, then colour in this happy scene.

Air Patrol

The PAW Patrol have got a new flying vehicle. What is its name? Find a small mirror, then hold it next to the letters below. Now look at the reflection.

The answer will be waiting for you in the glass!

Fly high, dream big!

THE AIR PATROLLER IS READY FOR TAKE-OFF!

Can you design a new flying badge?

Answers on page 69.

Tracker time

Tracker's amazing ears have picked up an interesting new sound. Listen! Where could the noise be coming from?

Choo Choo! Tickets please, all aboard!

a. Pup Park

b. Pet parlour

c. Train station

d. Jake's mountain

Answers on page 69.

Wally's day out

Can you find five differences between these two pictures of Wally and his pup pals?

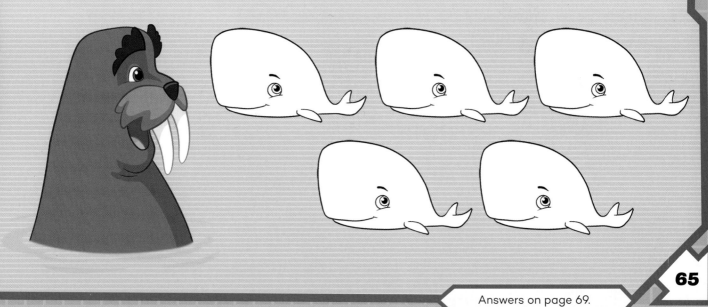

a

b

Colour in one of Wally's whale friends each time you spot a difference.

Answers on page 69.

Everest adventure!

When the PAW Patrol calls, Everest always comes to the rescue. The husky knows the best ways to go in the ice and snow.

Off the trail, Everest won't fail!

Did you know?

Everest lives on the mountain with Jake.

Everest is ... fun-loving and fearless.

Everest has ... top snowboarding skills.

Everest can ... slide down the slopes!

09

PUPPY POWER!

Snow **goggles** to show the way to go.

Quick-slide puppy paw holders.

Rocket-powered snowboard.

Pick up a penguin

Everest and Jake are teaching mountain rescue skills to their PAW Patrol friends! How many penguins is Marshall pulling in this sledge? Draw a circle around the correct number.

3

7

5

67

Answers on page 69.

Answers

Pages 8-9
To the skies!
b. Zuma

Page 11
Fun at the farm

Pages 12-13
Chase in the race!
Tricky tick test

1. b

2. c

3. a

Page 14
Save the day!

Pages 15-16
Seaside spotting
1. b   4. b
2. c   5. b
3. a   6. b

Page 17
Doggy day off
Rocky is feeling hungry.

Pages 28-29
Marshall on a mission!
Animal emergency

b

Page 31
Pup House puzzle
1. c

2. e

3. b

4. a

5. d

Page 33
Cal-amity!

c. Everest wears this badge.